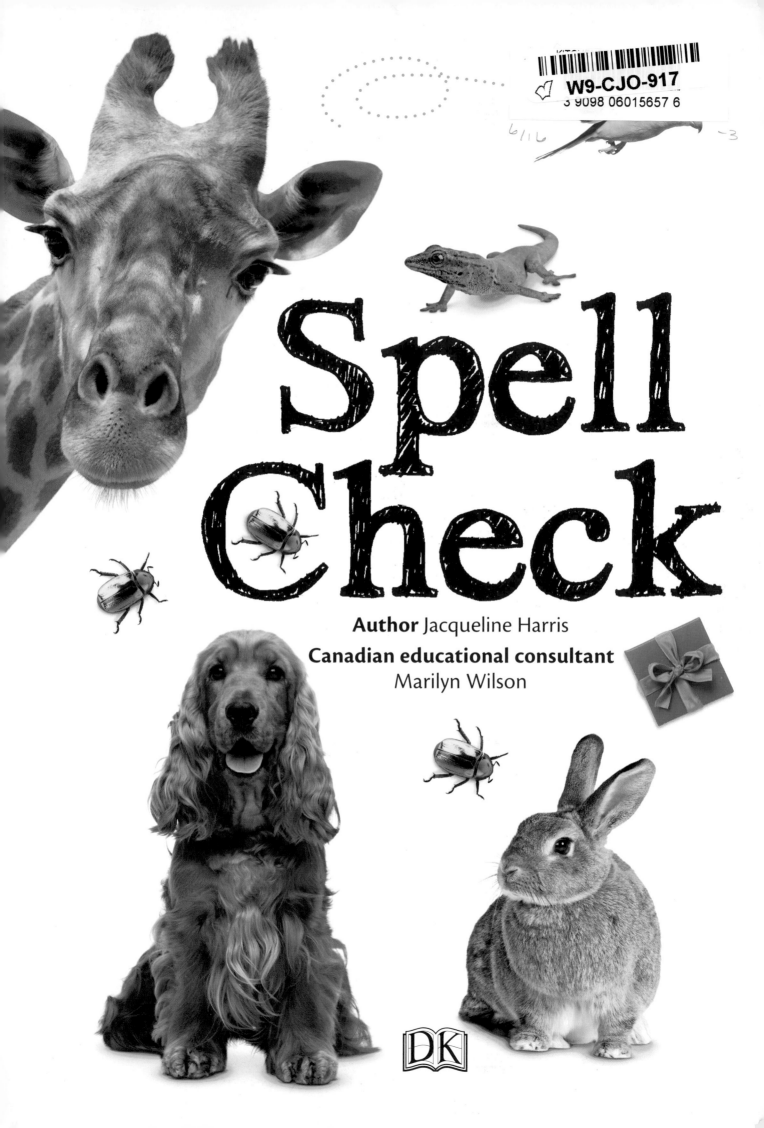

# Spell Check

**Author** Jacqueline Harris

**Canadian educational consultant**
Marilyn Wilson

# Contents

# Important note to you!

## Why learn to spell?

Spelling is an incredibly useful tool. Correct spelling allows other people to read and understand what you have written. Learning about spelling also gives you a bigger vocabulary to use in your writing and make it more interesting and powerful.

## Can't I rely on a dictionary or spell checker?

There are lots of reasons why learning to spell correctly is much better than relying on a book or a machine. Here are three of them:

1. If you have no idea how to spell a word, you will not be able to look it up in a dictionary, nor will the spell checker recognize which word you want.

2. Spell checkers also do not recognize mistakes with homophones (words that sound the same but are spelled differently) or typing mistakes like this regular one: "form" instead of "from."

3. Most importantly, neither a dictionary nor a machine will be able to tell you that there is a much better and more exciting word you could be using instead.

## Why do I need this book?

This book will give you the RULES for many common spellings, show you how the rules work, and provide examples. When you learn the spelling rules, you find the meanings of so many new words and you have words that can bring your writing to life. While there are a great many rules, there are also words that follow no rule at all and just have to be learned. This book will point out these EXCEPTIONS.

**How it works:**
nut + **s** = nut**s**
**Examples:**
squirrel → squirrel**s**
tree → tree**s**
stick → stick**s**
tail → tail**s**

Then you can practise the rules and test yourself with finding new words and links in spelling patterns on the ACTIVITY pages.

This book will also give you TIPS on how to learn spelling, because not everyone likes to learn in the same way. By the end, you will have found a few different ways that help YOU remember spellings, as well as helpful lists of words to practise called "Words to learn."

**Look out for the animals, because they're eager to help you and give examples about how the spelling rules work!**

# Meet the phonic families

I am Mar**lee**, a proud mother hen! Just look at my fluffy family of four chicks. Aren't they sweet? They are a bit noisy though! We are the **/ee/** sound family, but my chicks have names that have the sound spelled differently than mine. There's Peach, Eve, Bobby, and Finley.

## Phonics

A technical word for how sounds (phonemes) and letters (spelling patterns) make words. English has 44 different phonemes, and most of these have several different ways (at least) of spelling them.

Use what you know about **phonics** as your first step when trying to spell an unfamiliar word. Then see if the word looks right, and if not, try a different spelling pattern for a sound.

*Good idea!*

## Long vowel sounds

**/ai/** (tr**ai**n), **/ee/** (f**ee**t), **/igh/** (n**igh**t), **/oa/** (b**oa**t), **/oo/** (f**oo**d), **/u-e/** (t**u**b**e**)

## Short vowel sounds

**/a/** (h**a**t), **/e/** (p**e**t), **/i/** (s**i**t), **/o/** (c**o**t), **/u/** (h**u**t)

## Digraphs and trigraphs

When you have two letters together that make just one sound, it is called a **digraph**—for example **sh** in "ship." When you have three letters together making one sound, it is called a **trigraph**—for example **igh** in "high."

**CAN YOU** use your phonics knowledge to sound out and spell the names of these animals?

Start thinking!

# What is the plural of squirrel?

I am a very hungry squirrel. A hungry squirrel needs lots of nuts to eat. Nuts is the plural of nut. Plural means "more than one." Without plurals, I could only have one nut. Did I mention that I was hungry?

tails

RULE

## Just add an "s"

This, in a nutshell, is the first rule of making plurals. To form the plural of most nouns, add **s**.

legs

**nut**

**nuts**

## How it works:

nut + **s** = nut**s**

### Examples:

squirrel → squirrel**s**

tree → tree**s**

stick → stick**s**

tail → tail**s**

ears

lakes

foxes

boxes

sandwiches

lunches

watches

beaches

**RULE**

buses

glasses

cows

classes

dishes

schools

dresses

princes

toes

knees

princesses

## Add "es"

Many words are made plural with the addition of an **es**. This sounds like **/ez/**. To form the plural of nouns ending in **s**, **x**, **z**, or **ch**, just add **es**.

**grass**

**grasses**

## How it works:

bench + **es** = bench**es**

## Examples:

grass → grass**es**

buzz → buzz**es**

class → class**es**

pass → pass**es**

# Owls or owles?

Whoooooo wants to practise more plurals? Come on, it will be a hoot. Remember, if you add an **s** to a word and it sounds like **/ez/**, it is spelled **es**. Listen for the extra sound at the end.

## Fill in fun

**Complete the lists with either "s" or "es" to make plurals.**

1 goat, 3 ..goats.........     1 girl, 3 ........................

1 team, 3 ....................     1 weed, 3 ....................

1 toy, 3 ........................     1 patch, 3 ....................     1 night, 3 ....................

1 kiss, 3 .......................     1 bench, 3 ................     1 wish, 3 ....................

## The big finish!

**Try turning these nouns into plurals.**

witch .................................................

wand .................................................

cat .....................................................

spell ...................................................

wizard ...............................................

# Super silly sentences

**Cross out the wrong word in these sentences and write the correct one above.**

The owls sit on the branchs.

I spotted some foxs in the woods.

The magic potiones turned the tables into chocolate.

The witch lit the candles with some matchs.

We learned lots of spelles in our lessons.

We waved our magic wandes and the owl disappeared!

# Double up

**Rewrite this magic spell but make all the singular words plural.**

Note: You may need to change or cut out some other words, too.

The witch added an eye of a frog, a feather of a bird, a tail of a horse, and a scale of a fish.

......................................................................................................

......................................................................................................

......................................................................................................

# Sing a spelling

I am a noisy songbird, who knows a trick that may help you learn your spellings: turn the rule or a particular spelling into a rhyme or mini song.

Music is a useful way to learn, and a rhyme, tune, or rhythm can help you remember. Sing a tune with me!

Good idea!

## people

To the tune of Happy Birthday To You:

"p-e-o-p-l-e, p-e-o-p-l-e, p-e-o-p-l-e, that's how you spell people."

## plural rule

To the rhythm of Humpty Dumpty: "For most plurals, just add an **s**. That just means there is more than one. But some other plurals will sound like an **/ez/**. Then you will know that you must add **e-s**."

**CAN YOU pick a rhyme you know well?**

Make up a rhyme for spelling this word.

## surprise

*Start thinking!*

Turn this rule into a different rhyme.

## plural rule

# Why, wolf, y?

I am an inquisitive wolf cub, and enjoy exploring with the other babies. It's more fun when there are more than one! That's when the lone wolf becomes a pack of wolves. Howl!

## "y" to "i" then add "es"

If a word ends in **y**, the plural changes the **y** to an **i** before adding **es**. BUT for words ending in **ey**, **ay**, or **oy**, just add an **s**.

strawberry

strawberries

## How it works:

baby – **y** → i + **es** = bab**ies**

### Examples:

lady → lad**ies**

city → cit**ies**

strawberry → strawberr**ies**

## RULE

### "f" to "v"

If a word ends in **f**, the plural changes the **f** to a **v** before adding **es**.

Watch out for any noun that has the /**f**/ sound at the end of it—even if it is spelled **fe**, like in "life." The plural also ends with **ves.**

## How it works:

wolf − **f** → **v** + **es** = wol**ves**

### Examples:

calf → cal**ves**

knife → kni**ves**

life → li**ves**

wife → wi**ves**

centuries

ladies

families

skies

bodies

teddies

memories

halves

hooves

selves

wives

loaves

scarves

knives

lives

keys

journeys

monkeys

calves

calf

# Two's company

**Give these animals some company by making the plurals.**

dog .............................

bee .............................

duck .............................

fox .............................

# Word swap

**Rewrite these phrases, turning the words in bold into plurals.**

Note: You may need to change or cut out some other words, too.

A **wolf** in the dark **wood** .........................................................................

A **baby** in the **crib** .........................................................................

A **lady** with a **loaf** of bread .........................................................................

A **horseshoe** on the **hoof** .........................................................................

# Odd one out

Which of the words in each line is the odd one out when they are made plural? Circle the word.

dog        pig        (fish)

Fish is the odd one out because you add **es** not just **s** to make the plural.

calf        cow        bull

bear       canary     butterfly

puppy     fly        porcupine

# Time for a tune

Turn the rule about changing "y" to an "i" and adding "es" into a song.

You can either use one of the tunes you used on page 11 or try one of your favourite tunes.

# I'm not a regular sheep

I am a sheep and I don't follow the rules. On my own, I'm just me, a sheep. But when a flock of us get together, we are not sheeps, we are still sheep. It's not baa-d spelling, it's just that "sheep" is an irregular plural. Remember: If you can't sleep, don't count sheeps; count sheep.

sheep

Baaa!

hooves

RULE

## Stay the same

Some words, like "sheep," stay the same as singular and plural.

**Examples:**
sheep
moose
deer
aircraft
pants

sheep

hoof

# All change

Other words completely change when they become plural.

**Examples:**

mouse → mice

goose → geese

man → men

tooth → teeth

child → children

geese

woman

women

child

children

salmon

scissors

louse

lice

person

people

foot

feet

bison

moose

cactus

cacti

jeans

tights

# A herd of rhinos or rhinoes?

I belong to a herd of rhinos. We are one of a group of animals that have a vowel ending that's not an **e**. This means that we have our own rules for plurals. Don't get this wrong or we'll get angry and we'll charge!

## Add "s" or "es"

If a word ends in **a**, **i**, or **u**, just add an **s**. If a word ends in **o**, add an **es**. BUT this is not true for words like rhino, hippo, dodo, disco, and photo.

Watch out! There are some exceptions with words like "antenna," which become "antennae."

banana

bananas

**Examples:**

volcano → volcano**es**

tomato → tomato**es**

gnu → gnu**s**

cobra → cobra**s**

banana → banana**s**

gorilla → gorilla**s**

photo → photo**s**

## Note

My longer name is "rhinoceros" but in a herd, we can become a group of "rhinoceroses." What a mouthful! No wonder our name is often shortened.

## How it works:

rhino — rhino**ceros** →

rhino**ceros** or

rhino**ceroses**

## Examples:

photo — photo**graph** →

photo**graphs**

hippo — hippo**potamus** →

hippo**potami** or

hippo**potamuses**

banana

potato

potatoes

flamingo

flamingoes

photos

rhinos

volcanoes

tomatoes

buffaloes

taxis

zebras

sofas

llamas

kiwis

orchestras

dramas

gorillas

# Sort it out

## Write these animals in their plural form in the correct column:

monkey, moose, butterfly, mouse, fish, penguin, wallaby, fox, armadillo, snake, eagle, pony

| Just add "s" | Add "es" |
| --- | --- |
| .................................. | .................................. |
| .................................. | .................................. |
| .................................. | .................................. |
| .................................. | .................................. |
| .................................. | .................................. |

| Change to "ies" | Irregular |
| --- | --- |
| .................................. | .................................. |
| .................................. | .................................. |
| .................................. | .................................. |
| .................................. | .................................. |

# Animals' alphabet

**Think of an animal for every letter of the alphabet and write the name as if there are more than one of them.**

Check your spellings in a dictionary.

A ....................................................

B ....................................................

C ....................................................

D ....................................................

E ....................................................

F ....................................................

G ....................................................

H ....................................................

I ....................................................

J ....................................................

K ....................................................

L ....................................................

M ....................................................

N ....................................................

O ....................................................

P ....................................................

Q ....................................................

R ....................................................

S ....................................................

T ....................................................

U ....................................................

V ....................................................

W ....................................................

X ....................................................

Y ....................................................

Z ....................................................

# Does it look right?

Spelling can be a very prickly job! The spelling of some words follows the rules, but for other words you just have to learn how to spell them. To help you learn, just try to spell the word and see if it looks right.

And for an extra prickly tip: if it looks wrong then try again, maybe by using a different way of spelling the same sound.

Good idea!

## p o r c u p i n e

**por** is spelled just how it sounds, and **pine** follows the rules. But the middle bit sounds like **/q/**—**porqpine**. This doesn't look right! There would never be a **q** next to a **p**. So either look the word up in a dictionary or try again.

Follow these steps:

## Step 1

What sounds can you hear when you say the word? How many sounds can you hear? Are there any sounds that have two letters or more?

## Step 2

Try to spell the word yourself and then see if it looks right.

## Step 3

If it doesn't, try again, then check with an adult or in a dictionary.

**CAN YOU try spelling the names of these animals, using the three steps?**

*Start thinking!*

# Hopping around letters

I am a grasshopper and I have a challenge for you! I just can't keep still, and neither can the letters in my name. The letters want to hop around and make new words of all different lengths.

**How many different words can you make with the letters in "grasshopper"?**

**Good idea!**

Start off by working out the different digraphs you can use—for example **er**, **sh**, and **oe**. Can you find any others? Put them as headings in the boxes. Then see how many different words you can make using the letters.

**s h**

shape

rash

**e r**

o e

**g r a s s h o p p e r**

It might help to cut the letters out on a piece of paper and move them around, or use a piece of paper to try out spellings and see if they look right.

*Good idea!*

# Cats vs. dogs

I am a cat, who does regular cat-like things. I can walk and jump, and curl up to sleep. These action words are verbs that tell you what I'm actually doing.

## Add "ed" or "ing"

For regular verbs, just add **ed** at the end for the past tense, meaning it has already happened; and just add **ing** for the present tense, which means it is happening now.

## HOW it works:

walk + **ed** = walk**ed**

walk + **ing** = walk**ing**

## Examples:

jump → jump**ed**, jump**ing**

crawl → crawl**ed**, crawl**ing**

I am a dog, who does regular dog-like things, which are slightly different to cats. I can hug and rub, and drip from my mouth.

**RULE**

## Double up

For regular verbs with a short vowel sound in them, double the end consonant when in the past or present tense.

## HOW it works:

hug + **ed** = hug**ged**

hug + **ing** = hug**ging**

## Examples:

rub → rub**bed**, rub**bing**

drip → drip**ped**, drip**ping**

The exception to the doubling rule is for words that end with **x**. Never double **x**! mix → mix**ed**, mix**ing**

guard

guarding

guarded

appear

appeared

appearing

protect

protected

suggest

suggested

trip

tripped

skip

skipping

strapped

fix

fixed

fixing

# What makes pets amazing?

We are amazing pets. We can dance and dazzle, bounce and dive, explore and race. And what's more amazing is that all our verbs end with an **e**!

RULE

## Verbs ending with "e"

When a verb ends with **e**, take the **e** off and then add **ing** for the present tense, OR just add the **d** for the past tense.

racing

## How it works:

dance − **e** + **ing** = danc**ing**

dance + **d** = dance**d**

## Examples:

explore → explor**ing**, explore**d**

dazzle → dazzl**ing**, dazzle**d**

love → lov**ing**, love**d**

dive → div**ing**, dive**d**

dazzling

refuse

slide

breathe

exercise

notice

promise

surprise

suppose

type

continue

believe

complete

decide

describe

increase

guide

scare

save

## Note

Some strange animals can do things that don't follow this rule. Some verbs ending in **e** are irregular and completely change (see pages 32–33), and other verbs like "agree" become agree**d** or agree**ing**.

# Right or wrong?

**Cross out the regular verbs that are spelled wrong.**

jumped          danceing          growlling          bounced

fixxed          dived          joging          mixing

raced          explord

# Double or not

**Sort these verbs into the two columns.**
**Write them in the past tense.**

notice, hop, groan, like, slip, plan, share, enjoy, ask, use, stop

| Double the consonant for the past tense | Do not double the consonant for the past tense |
|---|---|
| ............................................ | ............................................ |
| ............................................ | ............................................ |
| ............................................ | ............................................ |
| ............................................ | ............................................ |
| ............................................ | ............................................ |
| ............................................ | ............................................ |
| ............................................ | ............................................ |

# Odd one out

**Which of the words in each line is the odd one out when they are in the past or present tense? Circle the word.**

walk        jump        (hop)

Hop is the odd one out because it is the verb that doubles the consonant in the past and present tense.

| | | |
|---|---|---|
| like | hug | hope |
| bake | pull | help |
| count | skip | grab |
| play | paint | run |

# Time challenge

**How many verbs can you think of in four minutes? Then turn the words you have written into the past tense.**

(If you have written irregular verbs—see pages 32–33—they don't follow the rules and completely change in the past tense.)
Remember: To spell the verbs, sound them out and use phonics to help you.

......................................        ......................................

......................................        ......................................

......................................        ......................................

......................................        ......................................

......................................        ......................................

......................................        ......................................

......................................        ......................................

# What makes a platypus irregular?

I am a duck-billed platypus and quite unusual. I'm a furry mammal but I have a duck's beak and lay eggs. You could say that I'm completely irregular and certainly don't follow the rules for being a mammal.

## Irregular verbs

Irregular verbs don't follow the rules when they change to the past tense. The only way to learn them is to remember them and say a sentence out loud and see if it sounds right.

### Examples:

drink → drank

say → said

make → made

come → came

throw → threw

## Note

Here are some more irregular examples that are useful to know!

## Examples:

know → knew
take → took
buy → bought
hear → heard
write → wrote
feed → fed
sleep → slept

eat

ate

are

were

see

saw

shake

shook

meet

met

catch

caught

bite

bit

sell

sold

speak

spoke

# How to compare elephants

I am the smallest elephant in the herd. I like to compare myself to my dad who is bigger and heavier than me. At the waterhole, I can be the wettest and the muddiest though. Watch out! I'll squirt you!

**biggest**

**big**

## "er" and "est"

Sound the trumpet! Here are the important rules. When comparing two things, add **er** to the word. When something is the topmost thing, then add **est** to the word.

## How it works:

tall → tall**er** → tall**est**

## Examples:

small → small**er** → small**est**

slow → slow**er** → slow**est**

weak → weak**er** → weak**est**

fast → fast**er** → fast**est**

bigger

## Add "r" or "st"

For words already ending in **e**, just add **r** or **st**.

For words with a short vowel sound, double the end consonant before adding the ending.

For words ending in a **y**, change to an **i** before adding the ending.

# Words to learn

older

oldest

longer

longest

broader

broadest

tiny

tinier

tiniest

lazy

lazier

laziest

deeper

deepest

straight

straighter

heavy

heaviest

### Examples:

large → larger → largest

big → bigger → biggest

wet → wetter → wettest

heavy → heavier → heaviest

happy → happier → happiest

large

larger

largest

# Who is the biggest?

Squeak! I'm surrounded by animals bigger than me, but I'm quicker than most. The tiger looks the scariest to me!

## You choose!

**Which word is the best fit? Cross out the other word.**

The hippo is **(larger/largest)** than the zebra.

The antelope can run **(faster/fastest)** than the bison.

The little monkey can climb into the **(higher/highest)** branches of the trees.

The water buffalo is the **(muddier/muddiest)** of all the animals at the waterhole.

The tiger is the **(fiercer/fiercest)** of all the big cats.

# Compare challenge

Write the correct label for the animals.

| smallest | | tallest | | youngest |

| heaviest |

# Fill in fun

Complete the lists by writing the words with the suffixes "er" and "est."

happy <u>happier, happiest</u>          scary ..................................................

loud .......................................................          large ..................................................

quiet ......................................................          noisy ..................................................

# What makes playful cubs fearless?

We are playful bear cubs, full of happiness and enjoyment as we search for honey. You can play, too, describing how things are happening by adding the suffixes **ment**, **ful**, **less**, and **ness** to words. Don't be fearful, be fearless like us!

## Suffixes and root words

Adding suffixes does not usually change the spelling of the root word.

## How it works:

care + **ful** → care**ful**

## Examples:

sad → sad**ness**

hope → hope**less**, hope**ful**

enjoy → enjoy**ment**

# Change "y" to "i"

For words ending in **y**, which have more than one syllable, change the **y** to an **i**.

## How it works:

happy – **y** → **i** + **ness** →

happ**iness**

## Examples:

merry → merr**iment**

creepy → creep**iness**

joy → joy**ful**

amuse → amuse**ment**

pain → pain**less**

bright

brightness

lonely

loneliness

achieve

achievement

develop

development

fear

fearful

fearless

cheer

cheerful

graceful

restless

breath

breathless

purposeful

# What's the ending?

## Choose a suffix

Choose the suffixes "ment," "ful," "less," or "ness" to add to each of these words to describe these lion cubs.

rest ...............................................

beauty ...........................................

enjoy ............................................

colour ..........................................

naughty ........................................

## Sentence challenge

Write a sentence using each of the following words.

purposeful ....................................................................................

................................................................................................

................................................................................................

excitement .................................................................................

................................................................................................

................................................................................................

harmless ....................................................................................

................................................................................................

................................................................................................

# Find the meaning

"ful" means full of
"less" means without
"ment" means as a result of an action
"ness" means a state of
Use these meanings to make one word.

without care   careless ............................................

without harm   ............................................

the state of being kind   ............................................

full of cheer   ............................................

move as a result of an action   ............................................

# Missing word

**Use the words made in the activity above.**
**Put the correct word into these sentences.**

They showed great ............................................ when they looked
after the bird.

She knew the snake was ............................................ because she had read
about it in a book.

Having the dog made the old man feel very ............................................ .

The cat watched the ............................................ of the bird and got
ready to pounce.

John made a big mess when painting the house because
he was ............................................ .

# Who nests here?

I'm a cuckoo and I'm too lazy to make my own nest so I lay my eggs in other birds' nests. I like the robin's nest, the warbler's nest, and the magpie's nest. The apostrophe shows whom the home belongs to and to how many.

cuckoo's wing

## Apostrophe

When something belongs to one thing or person, the possessive apostrophe (') is used followed by an **s**.

## How it works:

burrow of the rabbit →
the rabbit**'s** burrow

## Examples:

the cat**'s** basket
the bear**'s** den
the fox**'s** burrow

the cat's basket

cuckoo's tail

# Plural apostrophe

When something belongs to more than one thing or person, just the apostrophe is added after the plural.

Except for irregular plurals, when the apostrophe is still before the **s**.

## How it works:

hive of the bees → the bee**s'** hive

nest of the mice → the mice**'s** nest

## Examples:

the pig**s'** sty

the parrot**s'** perch

the children**'s** game

## Words to learn

stopped

really

because

better

clothes

morning

window

friends

animals

would

again

after

everyone

wanted

something

mother

place

cried

# Whose home?

Match the animals to their homes and write in the list underneath.

| kennel | hive | burrow |
|--------|------|--------|
| coop | aquarium | dovecot |
| stable | lodge | barn |

the dog's kennel ...............................................  .................................................................

.................................................................  .................................................................

.................................................................  .................................................................

.................................................................

# Right the wrong

**Put the apostrophe in the correct place in these sentences.**

The girl got the horses saddle from the rack.

The mices nest was snug and dry.

The pigs supper was some acorns, which it ate very quickly.

It is Ibrahims birthday today.

I went to the childrens playground with my friends.

The leopards fur is covered with a spotted pattern.

# Time challenge

**How quickly can you use an apostrophe to transform these phrases?**

The horse belonging to the girl    the girl's horse ....................................

The cats belonging to the ladies ....................................

The sty belonging to the pig ....................................

The fur belonging to the bear ....................................

The hooves belonging to the buffaloes ....................................

The lair belonging to the wolf ....................................

# How to spell the /igh/ in fly

I am a tiny fly, but I can fly really high just like a spy plane with my amazing eye. Oh my! Is that a mighty-sized pie, I spy?

## The /igh/ sound

There are several different ways you can spell the **/igh/** sound. With so many choices, try to spell a word and see if it looks right.

**How it works:**

igh → h**igh**

split digraph **i-e** → l**i**k**e**

**ie** → p**ie**

**eye** → **eye**

capital letter **I**

**ei** → h**ei**ght

**y** → sp**y**

**pie**

## Note

/igh/ is the most common sound the letter **y** makes at the end of words. But **y** can also make the /ee/ sound at the end of words, as in "happy."

**Examples:**
fly, try,
my, reply,
why, sky

replied

deny

decide

polite

prize

cried

surprise

guide

height

buy

by

bye

fried

pie

nice

comply

eye

slight

# Fill in fun

**Read the clues and then complete the missing letters in these words.**

Most birds can do this.

f_y

Make something bigger with a special piece of glass.

magn_fy

Follow instructions.

c_mply

Tell someone you did not do something.

de_y

**Use the missing letters to make the name of a fierce animal.**

...................................................................

# Time for a tune

**Learn to spell the word "specify" using a song.**

You can either use one of the tunes you used on page 11 or try one of your favourite tunes.

# You choose!

**Choose the right word to complete these sentences. Cross out the other word.**

The tiger cubs (**rely/reply**) on their mother.

The students (**supply/apply**) for the job.

The witnesses (**guide/identify**) the thief.

The desert was (**defy/dry**).

# Word sort

**Does the letter "y" make the sound /ee/ or /igh/? Sort these words into the two columns.**

happy, fry, ordinary, apply, supply, century, probably, why, imply, July, lazy, actually, rely

| /igh/ sound | /ee/ sound |
| --- | --- |
| | |
| | |
| | |
| | |
| | |
| | |
| | |

# Why are gorillas great?

I may look like a gentle giant, but I'm actually a great gorilla. It's all in the **g**'s. "Gentle" and "giant" have a soft **g** like a **/j/** sound, while "great" and "gorilla" each have a hard **/g/** sound. Grrr.

## The sound of "g"

The sound the **g** makes depends on the other letters it is next to, particularly vowels and the digraphs.

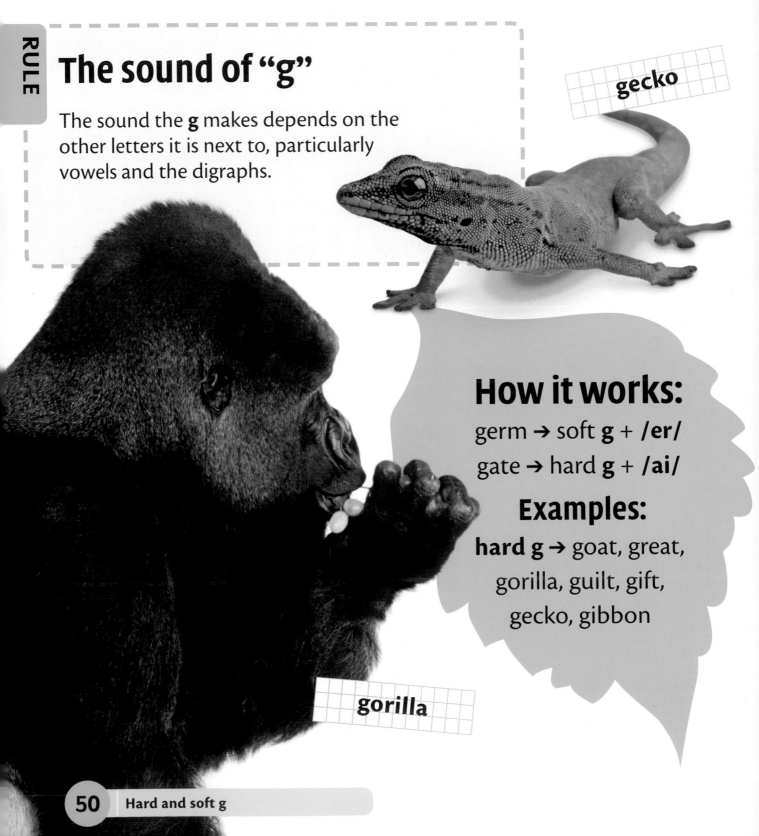

gecko

gorilla

## How it works:

germ → soft **g** + **/er/**

gate → hard **g** + **/ai/**

## Examples:

**hard g** → goat, great, gorilla, guilt, gift, gecko, gibbon

gerbil

**Examples:**

**soft g** → gerbil, giraffe, giant, ginger, gym

giraffe

group

grammar

guard

great

giraffe

gentle

fudge

bridge

dodge

magic

danger

energy

germ

gentleman

Egypt

gym

gymnastics

gorilla

# Why are giraffes and goats different?

Are you ready to solve this mystery? Complete the following detective work and then write your own clues so that you will remember this spelling.

## Clue 1

**Sort these words into two lists: soft "g" or hard "g."**

goat, giant, get, gum, giraffe, game, glad, gear, general, gem, germ, ginger, good, grape

| Soft "g" | Hard "g" |
|---|---|
| .................................... | .................................... |
| .................................... | .................................... |
| .................................... | .................................... |
| .................................... | .................................... |
| .................................... | .................................... |
| .................................... | .................................... |
| .................................... | .................................... |
| .................................... | .................................... |
| .................................... | .................................... |
| .................................... | .................................... |

# Clue 2

Add some of your own words to each list in Clue 1.

# Clue 3

Write some more words of your own that have the "g" somewhere other than the beginning—for example, "dodge" or "fling."

..................................................          ..................................................

..................................................          ..................................................

..................................................          ..................................................

..................................................

# Conclusion

Look at the detective's final report. Search out and underline the soft "g" and circle the hard "g" wherever they appear.

When I went to the zoo, I saw a huge range of animals. There were large

giraffes and a great gecko. The goats tried to get my gloves! Looking

suspicious was the giant panda, but I also suspected the grizzly bear,

which greeted me with a sort of smile as I gazed through the glass.

# Life at the North Pole

I am a polar bear, and I'm equipped and prepared for the extreme cold here at the North Pole. I've been watching the scientists working here though. They have to de-ice their vehicles before they can set out and there can be no mistakes, because it is dangerous to be out in the cold unprepared.

## Prefixes "un," "dis," or "mis"

When the prefix **un**, **dis**, or **mis** is added onto a word (the root), it does not change the spelling of the word, but only the meaning. The word turns into the opposite or negative of the original root word.

## How it works:

**un** + prepared → **un**prepared

**mis** + lead → **mis**lead

**dis** + like → **dis**like

## Examples:

appear → **dis**appear

fortunate → **un**fortunate

understood → **mis**understood

## Note

Not all words have a root word that still makes sense on its own. You can make a "mistake" but not a "take."

**Words to learn**

disappear

disapprove

disabled

disagree

discount

disconnect

misspell

mislay

misfit

misfortune

misunderstand

misuse

uncomfortable

uncommon

unable

uneasy

undo

uneven

# Fill in fun

**Add the correct prefixes "un," "dis," or "mis" to the incomplete words in the following paragraph.**

The scientists came to study the polar bear, whose habitat is slowly ........appearing. They were ........happy about what they .........covered. While they were ........certain of the exact problem, it was clear that there was no .........take; the polar bears were becoming rarer.

# What's the opposite?

?

**Use "un," "dis," or "mis" to make these words mean the opposite.**

dress ...........dress

comfort ...........comfort

behave ...........behave

understand ...........understand

connect ...........connect

?

?

# All change!

**Rewrite each of these sentences, changing its meaning.**

I like fruit. I dislike fruit.

My brother agreed with me.

........................................................................................

The rider mounted the horse.

........................................................................................

**Write one sentence of your own using a "mis," "dis," or "un" word used in "What's the opposite?"**

........................................................................................

........................................................................................

........................................................................................

........................................................................................

# Word bank

**Here are some great words you could use in your writing. Find the definition of each of them and then impress your teacher by using them in your writing.**

disgruntled ........................................................................................

misfortune ........................................................................................

unkempt ........................................................................................

# An elephant never forgets

They say an elephant never forgets anything. **Mnemonics** is a very tricky word for a way of remembering some of the more complicated spellings.

A **mnemonic** uses each of the letters in a word to give you a reminder of the spelling.

Good idea!

## because

**b**ig **e**lephants **c**an't **a**lways **u**se **s**mall **e**xits

## rhythm

**r**hythm **h**as **y**our **t**wo **h**ips **m**oving

## necessary

it is ne**ces**sary to have one
**c**ollar but two **s**leeves

**CAN YOU create a mnemonic for each
of these words?**
Will you still remember them in a few days' time?

## guard

## answer

## occasion

# How do desert snakes survive?

SSSs. It is exxxxceptionally hot here in the dessssert. I am a rattlessssnake and I sssssleepily sssstay coiled under a rock until sssslithering sssswiftly out to hunt once the ssssun hassss gone down.

## Suffix "ly"

The suffix **ly** turns an adjective into an adverb, so the word describes the action rather than the object. For most adjectives, just add **ly** to turn it into an adverb.

## How it works:

slow + **ly** → slow**ly**

## Examples:

quiet + **ly** → quiet**ly**

unfortunate + **ly** → unfortunate**ly**

glides
stealthily

slides
swiftly

## Adding "ly"

For words ending in **y**, the **y** changes to **i** before adding the **ly**.

For words that end in **le**, drop the **le** to add **ly**.

uncoils gracefully

## How it works:
angry − **y** → **i** + **ly** → angr**ily**
possible − **le** + **ly** → possib**ly**

## Examples:
happy → happ**ily**
easy → eas**ily**
comfortable → comfortab**ly**
horrible → horrib**ly**

## Words to learn

properly
furiously
splendidly
carefully
smoothly
bravely
possibly
comfortably
easily
horribly
lightly
friendly
regularly
seriously
probably
accidentally
occasionally
recently

# How do insects behave?

Buzz! The bees are buzzing angrily. The ants are marching briskly. How are the other insects in the garden behaving?

## Lively labelling

**Complete the labels on the picture to describe how you think the creatures are acting, using adverbs with "ly."**

butterflies fluttering
.....................................

bees buzzing
.....................................

beetles scuttling
.....................................

# Missing word

Add the adverbs to these sentences, picking the correct one from the list below.

| quietly | possibly | accidentally |
| --- | --- | --- |
| lightly | bravely | |

Bob spoke ..................................... .

The butterfly landed ..................................... on the flower petal.

The man ..................................... knocked the glass over, and it broke into a thousand pieces.

Harry ..................................... attacked the wasp before it stung the baby.

Tomorrow I may ..................................... be going to the park, but I am not sure.

# All change!

**Change these adjectives into adverbs.**

happy .....happily.....................     peculiar .....................................

naughty .....................................     regular .....................................

special .....................................     careful .....................................

strange .....................................     easy .....................................

surprising .....................................     sudden .....................................

# What's your position, pigeon?

I am a pigeon, but you won't find me in a park or a station because I'm a clever racing pigeon. Whatever my location, I can find my way back home. So to avoid confusion, look out for my identification tag.

## The /shun/ sound

The **/shun/** sound is mostly (but not always) spelled **sion** after the **/l/**, **/r/**, **/s/**, and **/n/** sounds. Otherwise the **/shun/** sound is spelled **tion**.

action

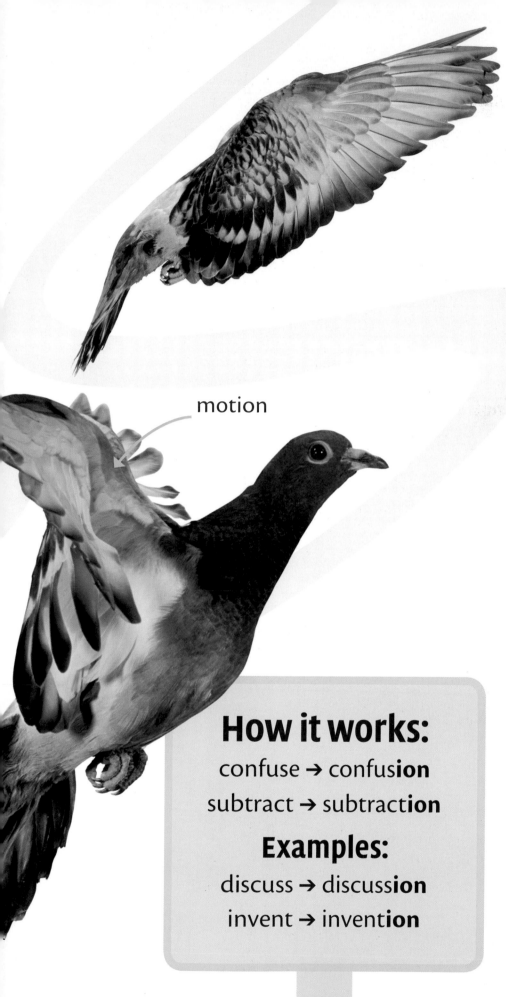

motion

## How it works:

confuse → confus**ion**

subtract → subtract**ion**

## Examples:

discuss → discuss**ion**

invent → invent**ion**

station

information

position

mention

imagination

fiction

addition

subtraction

multiplication

division

confusion

expression

invention

discussion

reception

description

creation

education

# Fact or fiction?

**Look at the list of stories that all feature animals. Then answer the questions.**

> **Three Billy Goats Gruff**     **Goldilocks and the Three Bears**
> **Three Little Pigs**     **Alice in Wonderland**     **Chicken Little**

Who went into the bears' house without permission?

..........................................................................................

Who had a very strong imagination so was not surprised to see a white rabbit with a watch?

..........................................................................................

What animal does the hungry troll positioned under a bridge want to eat?

..........................................................................................

Who created confusion by thinking that the sky had fallen in?

..........................................................................................

What was the wolf's mission when he blew down the houses?

..........................................................................................

# Happy endings

*tion* *sion* *tion* *sion*

**Add the correct suffix to these words, using "tion" or "sion."**

prevent ..prevention..............    create ...............................

discuss ...............................    describe ...............................

imagine ...............................    express ...............................

authorize ...............................    revise ...............................

# Word bank

**Here are some interesting words. Find the definition of each of them and then use each word in a sentence.**

confusion .................................................................

.................................................................

information .................................................................

.................................................................

invention .................................................................

.................................................................

subtraction .................................................................

.................................................................

education .................................................................

.................................................................

# How are you today, grey horse?

I am a very special horse because I pull the Queen's carriage in parades for important occasions. There are eight horses like me and we have very fine reins. At the start of her reign, the Queen was drawn in a carriage pulled by white horses, but we are beige or grey.

## The /ai/ sound

There are several different ways you can spell the **/ai/** sound. With so many choices, try to spell a word and see if it looks right.

eight

## How it works:

**ai** → tr**ai**n

**ay** → pl**ay**

the split digraph **a-e** → m**a**k**e**

**ei** → **ei**ght

**ey** → th**ey**

**a** → **a**corn

**ea** → br**ea**k

## Note

The digraphs **ai** or **ei** are never at the end of a word, but **ay** or **ey** are used at the end of a word.

**ay** is sometimes found in the middle of a word, too, like in "crayon."

they

grey

say

rein

beige

apron

sleigh

weight

eight

made

scrape

veil

dismay

paint

remain

translate

obey

escape

# Missing words

**Fill in the missing words to complete the description of the horses.**

| grey | eight | they | sleigh |
|---|---|---|---|
| reins | neighing | mane | stable |

These are fine ........................................ coloured horses, each with long

........................................ for the riders to hold. In winter, when it is snowy,

they sometimes pull a ........................................ . They make a loud noise

called ........................................ . ........................................ stay in a

........................................ at night and there are ........................................ stalls

altogether.  Each one has a beautifully cared for ........................................ .

# Sound families

**Begin a list of the words with different spellings of the /ai/ sound.**

| ai | ay | a |
|---|---|---|
| rain | stay | agent |
| ........................ | ........................ | ........................ |
| ........................ | ........................ | ........................ |

| ei | a-e | ey |
|---|---|---|
| beige | snake | they |
| ........................ | ........................ | ........................ |
| ........................ | ........................ | ........................ |

# Add the labels

Label each of the pictures. Each word has the /ai/ sound, but which spelling does it use?

..............................     ..............................     ..............................

..............................

..............................

..............................

..............................

# Is that a fowl or foul on the field?

I am a fowl, but don't confuse me with a foul between players on a football field. Otherwise you will be saying there was a duck on the field! Don't confuse me for a foul rainy day either, or else you'll be saying it's pouring with ducks!

## Homophones

Homophones are words that sound the same but are spelled differently and have different meanings. The only way you can work out these spellings is to learn them and learn their meanings.

### How it works:
fowl / foul

### Examples:
rein / reign

right / write

## Note

It is important to pick the right homophone because a computer would not be able to pick up on its spell check if this was not the right word.

tail (not tale)

feet (not feat)

to

too

two

there

their

they're

bear

bare

write

right

by

buy

eight

ate

here

hear

peace

piece

# Dear deer

*to? too? to? two?*

**Help deer by filling in the correct "to," "too," or "two" in the gaps in her letter!**

Dear deer,

How are you? I have been meaning ............ write ........... you for ............ weeks now, but I have been ............ busy at school. We have been learning all about homophones. How are things in the forest? If you'd like ............ catch up, meet me at ............ o'clock. Bring your friends the squirrels, ............

Hello!

From me!

*too?*

*to?* *two?*

---

# You choose!

**Choose the right homophone to complete these sentences.**

The boat sailed in (**fare/fair**) weather.

Dad (**mist/missed**) the train to work.

The boy ties a (**not/knot**) with his shoelaces.

The tired storekeeper took a (**break/brake**).

The lion had a majestic (**main/mane**).

# Match up!

Match the words below to the correct picture.

knight

flower

hair

bare

hare

bear

night

flour

# Silly sentences

Correct the mixed-up homophones in these silly sentences.

I couldn't wait to meat my friends. ...............................................................

Because I overslept, I mist the bus. ...............................................................

I had a long weight for the next bus. ...............................................................

The mouse got his tale caught. ...............................................................

# I'm an international sea turtle

I am a sea turtle. Welcome to my watery world. I may seem antisocial, but I'm an international traveller and I migrate hundreds of kilometres. I automatically follow the currents from USA to Indonesia and back again. Oh no! I can see a plastic bag littering the seabed and damaging the environment. If only that bag had been recycled!

RULE

## Prefixes and root words

Each of the prefixes **anti**, **auto**, **inter**, **re**, and **sub** comes from Latin. They each have a meaning that changes the meaning of the root word they are attached to.

## How it works:

**anti** = against or opposite →
**anti**social = not wanting the company of others

## Examples:

**auto** = the same or by itself → **auto**biography = a book about yourself

**inter** = between → **inter**national = involving different countries

**re** = again → **re**arrange = arrange it again differently

**sub** = beneath or below → **sub**marine = below the water

redo

refresh

return

reappear

redecorate

antidote

antisocial

autograph

automobile

automatic

subheading

submerge

submarine

interactive

interest

internal

interrupt

international

## Note

Often the root words are not proper words by themselves, for example, like "interrupt"—there is no such word as "rupt"!

## Examples:

**re**act

**anti**septic

**auto**matic

**inter**net

**sub**way

# Match up!

Match the prefixes to the ends of words to make complete words.

| Prefix | End of words | Completed words |
|---|---|---|
| anti | rupt | ............................................... |
| auto | merge | ............................................... |
| inter | biotic | ............................................... |
| re | turn | ............................................... |
| sub | matic | ............................................... |

# You choose!

**Choose the correct word in each of these sentences. Cross out the other word.**

I am going to (**reinvent/recycle**) these bottles.

When Suzy kept talking, the teacher asked her to please not (**interrupt/interval**) in the middle of the lesson.

In the intermission of a show, you can buy (**reforms/refreshments**).

The famous film star was asked for his (**autobiography/autograph**).

The crocodile was completely (**substantial/submerged**) under the water.

# Which one?

**Choose a prefix that can be added to the words in each row to make new words. Write the complete words.**

| Prefixes: | re | sub | anti | auto | inter |
|-----------|----|----|------|------|-------|

| | | | |
|--------|--------|--------|------------------------------------|
| cepted | act | lock | ................................................................. |
| tract | marine | ject | ................................................................. |
| cracy | pilot | mobile | ................................................................. |
| affirm | cord | heat | ................................................................. |
| social | climax | dote | ................................................................. |

# Word bank

**Choose four words with its prefix from the list above.**

For each word, find out what it means and write it in a sentence.

.........................................................................................

.........................................................................................

.........................................................................................

.........................................................................................

.........................................................................................

.........................................................................................

.........................................................................................

# How to remember the echidna

I am an echidna. I'm a very unusual type of creature that lives in Australia. You may never have heard of me before, and my name is certainly a very tricky word to spell. So here are some ideas that might help you remember my name.

**Good idea!**

Have a picture in your head of the word as well as the animal so that it sticks in your brain and looks familiar.

**Write the word ten times.**

**e c h i d n a**

echidna, echidna, echidna, echidna, echidna, echidna, echidna, echidna, echidna, echidna

**Think!** This animal looks a bit like a hedgehog.

**Split up the word into pieces.**

**e - c h i d - n a**

Use phonics, although this word does not sound the same as it is spelled.

**Turn the word into a picture.**

## e**ch**i**d**na

It has tall letters in the middle and shorter ones either side.
Notice the word **hid** in the middle.

**CAN YOU follow these three steps with these words?**

## country

## gardening

# Watch out for the rat!

I am the rat in separate. Separate is one of the most commonly misspelled words. Even adults do not always know how to spell it!

To remember that it's an **/ar/** sound, not an **/er/** sound, in the middle of sep**arat**e, remember **a rat**!

Good idea!

---

**Sound out the word.**

s – e – p – ar – a-e – t

There's a split digraph near the end of this word.

---

**Find the word within.**

s e p - a-rat- e

**Write the word ten times.**

**s e p a r a t e**

separate, separate, separate, separate, separate,

separate, separate, separate, separate, separate

**CAN YOU sound these words out and find the hidden word?**

**p e c u l i a r**

**b u s i n e s s**

**d i s a p p o i n t**

# Let's talk!

"Who's a pretty boy, then?"
That's me! I'm a talkative parrot. I don't use formal words. I've learned to talk using contractions. They're very useful for chatty birds like me.

## Contractions

A contraction is when two words (or more) are joined together and parts of the word are left out. The missing part is replaced with an apostrophe.

## How it works:

I + **a**m → I'm

## Examples:

do n**o**t → don't

they **a**re → they're

must n**o**t → mustn't

can**no**t → can't

we w**i**ll → we'll

## Note

Using contractions are a very casual way of writing, and if it is a piece of writing, such as a formal letter or a piece of information, there should not be any contractions in the work.

didn't

couldn't

you'd

what's

I'm

let's

they're

won't

should've

o'clock

we're

how'd

doesn't

haven't

I'll

isn't

aren't

it'll

# Cat rescue

**Change the contractions to full words to correct this class's newspaper report about a cat that was stuck in a tree.**

Yesterday at our school **we'd** ......................... seen a cat.

Our teacher said we **shouldn't** ......................... scare the cat but one boy

**didn't** ......................... listen and the cat ran up a tree. Our teacher said

we **mustn't** ......................... climb the tree to rescue the cat because we **won't**

......................... be able to get down, but Freya said **she's** .........................

a good climber and **she'd** ......................... be able to get the cat.

**She's** ......................... a very good climber and she did climb the tree.

I thought the cat might get frightened but **it'd** ......................... sat

watching us all and **wasn't** ......................... at all scared. Clever Freya

managed to get the cat down safely and our teacher said **she'd**

......................... been very brave.

# One-minute challenge

**Can you turn the following words into a contraction within a minute?**

he is ...........................................

do not ...........................................

that will ...........................................

could not ...........................................

# Sentence challenge

**Write a sentence for each of the following contractions.**

there's ..................................................................................

..................................................................................

isn't ..................................................................................

..................................................................................

o'clock ..................................................................................

..................................................................................

shouldn't ..................................................................................

..................................................................................

where'll ..................................................................................

..................................................................................

# You choose!

**Some contractions are also homophones that are often used wrongly. Choose the right spelling in each sentence. Cross out the wrong words.**

I've got **(your/you're)** book by mistake.

**(They're/There/Their)** going to the farm by bus.

**(Whose/Who's)** coat is that?

**(Its/It's)** a really sunny day today.

# Word art

I am a dolphin and I love to **leap** and **twirl**. My name is tricky to spell as it has a **ph** and not an **f** in it.

Turn the word you are learning to spell into a picture to help you remember it.

**Good idea!**

**dolphin**

dolphin

**tremor**

tremor

**squirrel**

CAN YOU turn these words into a picture?

**bounce**

**rainbow**

# Is it a cat or a civet?

I am a civet. Don't confuse me with a cat!
I'm a completely different animal. My body
is a different shape than a cat. My name
begins with a different sound, too.
Although civet is spelled with a **c**,
the sound it makes is **/s/**.

RULE

## The letter "c"

The letter **c** makes the widest range
of sounds in the English language.
 **/k/** → **c**at
 **/s/** → **c**ivet
 **/q/** → **c**ue
 **/sh/** → spe**c**ial
 **/x/** → a**cc**ess

# Sound change

The letters or letter strings following the **c** changes the sound the **c** makes.

## How it works:

**c** + **a**, or **o** = /k/ → **ca**t or **co**t

## Examples:

**c** + **e**, **i**, or **y** = /s/ → **ce**iling, **ci**vet, **cy**cle

**c** + **ia**, **ea**, or **io** = /sh/ → spe**cia**l, o**cea**n, suspi**cio**us, magi**cia**n

**c** + **c** = /x/ → a**cc**ept

**c** + **ue** = /q/ → **cue**

cycle

calendar

special

centre

century

certain

caught

circle

complete

continue

decide

describe

experience

increase

sentence

actually

bicycle

exercise

difficult

# Word sort

*carrot    cardigan    accident    magician*

## Sort these words into the sound the "c" makes.

carrot, cardigan, accident, magician, column, disco, cylinder, cue, access, celebrity, ocean, mercy, octopus, Canada, cereal, except, December, celery

| c = /k/ | c = /s/ | c = /sh/ | c = /q/ | c = /x/ |
|---------|---------|----------|---------|---------|
| ............... | ............... | ............... | ............... | ............... |
| ............... | ............... | ............... | ............... | ............... |
| ............... | ............... | ............... | ............... | ............... |
| ............... | ............... | ............... | ............... | ............... |
| ............... | ............... | ............... | ............... | ............... |
| ............... | ............... | ............... | ............... | ............... |
| ............... | ............... | ............... | ............... | ............... |
| ............... | ............... | ............... | ............... | ............... |
| ............... | ............... | ............... | ............... | ............... |
| ............... | ............... | ............... | ............... | ............... |

## Add some of your own words to each list.

# Word art

**Choose a word from each list and create a word picture.**

Can you include in each picture what sound the "**c**" makes to help you remember the rules?

# Ssh for the little lamb

In the springtime, I leap and run around the field. I'm just a little lamb so then I need to take a rest. Quiet, please! You can't hear all the letters in my name. The **b** is silent. You'd never know it was there.

## Silent letters

The only way to spell words with silent letters correctly is to find a way of remembering that silent letter. Start by actually sounding out the letter.

gnome

## How it works:

friend ➜ **i** is silent ➜ say fr**i**-end

## Examples:

**k**night ➜ **k** is silent ➜ say **k**-night
**g**nome ➜ **g** is silent ➜ say **g**-nome
i**s**land ➜ **s** is silent ➜ say i**s**-land
choc**o**late ➜ the second **o** is silent
➜ say choc-**o**-late

## Note

Look out for unstressed or silent letters in all sorts of words.

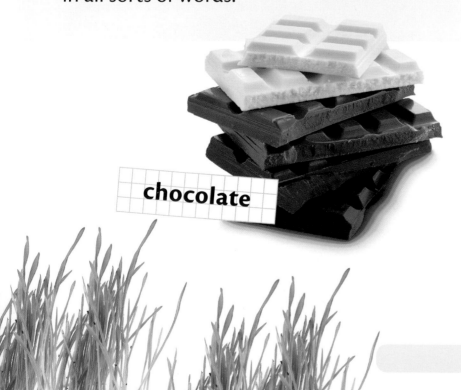

chocolate

thumb

scissors

friend

knight

lamb

column

Autumn

island

difference

definite

dictionary

January

February

medicine

knife

jewellery

vegetable

family

# Quiz master

**All the answers to these questions have a word with a silent letter.**

Make sure you do not leave the letter out when you write the answer!
Note: Check the spelling of your answers with a dictionary or an adult.

What is a baby cow called?

........................................................................

Which is the second month of the year?

........................................................................

Which subject at school includes the study of weather?

........................................................................

A carrot is a type of what?

........................................................................

Which two things can you use for cutting something?

........................................................................

What is a piece of land entirely surrounded by water?

........................................................................

Which delicious sweet brown food melts when it gets too hot?

........................................................................

# Letter hunt

Use a coloured pencil to highlight the unstressed or silent letters in each word.

wrinkle

guide

gnash

sandwich

wrapping

disguise

interest

kneel

foreign

climb

science

castle

listen

biscuit

# Word bank

Here are some words with silent letters. Find the definition of each of them and then use each word in a sentence.

wreckage ..............................................................................

..............................................................................

chaos ..............................................................................

..............................................................................

doubt ..............................................................................

..............................................................................

# What are your thoughts?

I am a shire horse. Look how big and strong I am. I used to pull the plow on farms. As I worked through the day, I thought about returning to my stable at night for my food and water in the trough. I would eat and drink until I'd had enough.

## Letter strings

**ough** is a very common spelling pattern. Although the same four letters are together, they make a different sound, depending on the word.

trough

## How it works:

/ow/ → b**ough**

/off/ → tr**ough**

/oo/ → thr**ough**

/o/ → th**ough**

/uff/ → en**ough**

/aw/ → th**ough**t

## More strings

**igh**, **ear**, and **ie** are other common spelling patterns that make several sounds. Watch out for these in words!

## Words to learn

height

weight

pear

earn

field

niece

thieves

tried

cough

enough

thought

through

though

thorough

tough

rough

dough

trough

## How it works:

/igh/ → h**igh**

/ai/ → we**igh**t

/ear/ → h**ear**

/air/ → p**ear**

/ur/ → **ear**n

/igh/ → p**ie**

/ee/ → ni**ec**e

pie

pear

# Word sort

**Put the words in the correct column for the sound of the letter string "ough."**

ought, bought, rough, cough, borough, dough, slough, although, trough, thorough, enough, tough, thought, through

| /off/ | /uff/ | /o/ | /aw/ | /oo/ |
|-------|-------|-----|------|------|
| .................... | .................... | .................... | .................... | .................... |
| .................... | .................... | .................... | .................... | .................... |
| .................... | .................... | .................... | .................... | .................... |
| .................... | .................... | .................... | .................... | .................... |
| .................... | .................... | .................... | .................... | .................... |

# Memory mnemonics

**Write mnemonics (see pages 58–59) for two of the words above.**

.................................................................................................

.................................................................................................

.................................................................................................

.................................................................................................

.................................................................................................

.................................................................................................

.................................................................................................

.................................................................................................

# Picture this

**Create a word art using one of the words on page 100.**

# Rhyme time

**Write a rhyming word for each of these words.**

Note: The spelling of the rhyming words does not have to be the same because it is only the sound that matters.

pear  hair ............................................

weight ............................................

learn ............................................

sigh ............................................

through ............................................

bough ............................................

tough ............................................

fear ............................................

cough ............................................

# which sow?

I am a sow and the proud mother to my many little piglets. See how they are very happily playing next to me in our sty. Nearby, the farmer is plowing the field ready to sow some seeds. I hope the noise won't upset my piglets.

**sow**

## Homographs

Homographs are words that are spelled the same but are often pronounced differently and have different meanings. You can only tell which word is which when they are in a sentence.

**bow**

## How it works:

sow = to plant seeds

sow = female pig

## Examples:

bow = bend over to show thanks

bow = a knot for tying shoelaces or decorative ribbon

wind

bow

read

saw

tear

can

change

match

park

rock

sink

fine

minute

row

wave

wound

bass

down

## Note

Sometimes homographs are pronounced the same but still mean different things.

change

## How it works:

change = to do something differently

change = money given if you have overpaid

## Examples:

wave = move of a hand to say hello or goodbye

wave = arch of water sweeping onto a beach

# Silly sentences

**How silly can you get? Write a sentence that uses both meanings of the following homographs.**

For example: The **bass** sang in a deep **bass** voice.

tear ..............................................................................................................

sink ..............................................................................................................

rock ..............................................................................................................

wound ..........................................................................................................

minute ..........................................................................................................

# Picture puzzler

**Choose two of these homographs and draw a picture for both meanings.**

| park | match | row | ring | court |
|------|-------|-----|------|-------|

# Match the meaning

**Match the homograph underlined in the sentence to its correct definition.**

Tick (✓) the correct definition.

| Sentence | Definitions | Tick |
|---|---|---|
| I got a **fine** when my library book was late back. | Everything is ok | |
| | A charge made for overdue items or illegally parked cars | |
| When he went under a low branch he had to **duck**. | A water bird, often seen on ponds | |
| | A verb meaning to move your head down quickly | |
| The **wind** was blowing wildly through the trees. | A strong gust of air | |
| | A verb meaning to roll up or turn the movements on a clock | |
| A **saw** was used to cut the logs smaller. | The past tense of the verb to see | |
| | A sharp, serrated edged cutting tool | |
| When I returned home from school, I wanted to **watch** my favourite TV program. | A small clock worn on the wrist | |
| | A verb meaning to look at | |

# When does two become one?

We may be tiny creatures but we all have something in common. No, it's not that we all have six legs and wings—there's something else as well. The clues are in our names: butterfly, honeybee, horsefly, dragonfly, and ladybug. Each of our names is a compound word.

butterfly

## Compound words

A compound word is when two words are put together to make a new word. The spelling of both the original words stays the same. When a word is added to another, the new compound word has a different meaning.

ladybugs

## How it works:

dragon + fly → dragonfly

## Examples:

ear + wig → earwig

silk + worm → silkworm

earth + worm → earthworm

Buzz! I'm back to my beehive!

honeybee

earwig

earthworm

housefly

thumbnail

bluebell

birthday

everyone

somewhere

anybody

playground

football

downstairs

goalkeeper

weekend

breakfast

sideboard

backbone

sunshine

## Note

Some of us see with compound eyes. Compound means "when things are put together," and some of us have amazing eyes made up of hundreds of cells.

dragonfly

# Mixed up pictures

Join any two words from the list below to make nine new types of insects. Then draw some of them.

| fly | body | foot | fast | bell | saw | water | earth |
| lady | ball | bed | worm | bug | glow | bee | see |
| flower | break | dragon | blue | fall | no | | |

foot + fly → footfly

.............................................................

.............................................................

.............................................................

.............................................................

.............................................................

.............................................................

.............................................................

.............................................................

# Match up!

**Create 12 compound words by joining a word from each list.**

| List 1 | | | |
|---|---|---|---|
| goal | sun | blue | half |
| birth | every | paint | break |
| up | any | back | fair |

| List 2 | | | |
|---|---|---|---|
| stairs | bell | one | keeper |
| day | fast | body | brush |
| bone | shine | time | ground |

..................................................   ..................................................

..................................................   ..................................................

..................................................   ..................................................

..................................................   ..................................................

..................................................   ..................................................

..................................................   ..................................................

..................................................   ..................................................

# Out and about

**Look for some compound words around you and compile a list of the ones you have seen.**

For example: Place names are sometimes compound words, and there may be some in the books you are reading.

..................................................   ..................................................

..................................................   ..................................................

..................................................   ..................................................

..................................................   ..................................................

..................................................   ..................................................

# Do beetles scuttle or scuttal?

We are busy beetles. We scuttle everywhere on our six little legs. Watch out! We may tickle if we crawl across your hand.

## "le" or "al"

The **le** is the most frequent spelling for this sound at the end of words. If in doubt always choose **le**, rather than **al**.

eagle

## How it works:

crump + **le** → crump**le**

## Examples:

examp + **le** → examp**le**

tab + **le** → tab**le**

eag + **le** → eag**le**

# When to double

If the word has a short vowel sound followed by one consonant, the consonant is usually doubled before adding **le**. (Don't forget: some consonants are never doubled such as **j** or **h**.)

If the word has a short vowel sound followed by two consonants, just add **le**.

If the word has a long vowel sound, or digraph, followed by one consonant, just add **le**.

## Words to learn

example

little

people

table

middle

needle

uncle

simple

bicycle

eagle

startle

circle

possible

probable

material

natural

occasional

special

## How it works:

ap + **p** + **le** → ap**ple**

sing + **le** → sing**le**

spark + **le** → spark**le**

## Examples:

mid**dle**, pud**dle**, cand**le**, beet**le**

apple

# Double or not

**Write the answers to these clues. All the answers end in "le."**

Remember: Only some consonants are doubled
before adding **le**. (The first letter has been provided.)

The name of this type of insect.

b .............................................

An octopus has eight of these.

t ..............................................

A hedgehog has lots of these.

p .............................................

The name of this sea creature.

t ..............................................

A penguin walks like this.

w .............................................

# Time for a tune

**Look back at the two rules about words ending in "le" on pages 110 and 111 and turn them into a tune to help you remember them.**

You can either use one of the tunes you used on page 11, or try one of your favourite tunes.

# Word collection

**Add more words under each column for each of these word endings.**

| -ckle | -able |
|---|---|
| crackle | table |
| ........................................ | ........................................ |
| ........................................ | ........................................ |
| ........................................ | ........................................ |
| ........................................ | ........................................ |
| ........................................ | ........................................ |
| ........................................ | ........................................ |
| ........................................ | ........................................ |

| -ible | -dle |
|---|---|
| horrible | candle |
| ........................................ | ........................................ |
| ........................................ | ........................................ |
| ........................................ | ........................................ |
| ........................................ | ........................................ |
| ........................................ | ........................................ |
| ........................................ | ........................................ |

# I'm an expressive chimp

Can you guess how I'm feeling? I can make this face. . . and this face. . . and this face. Do you think my grimace is happy or sad? I could be overjoyed or gloomy, glad or miserable. There are so many words to describe how you think I may be feeling, so choose carefully.

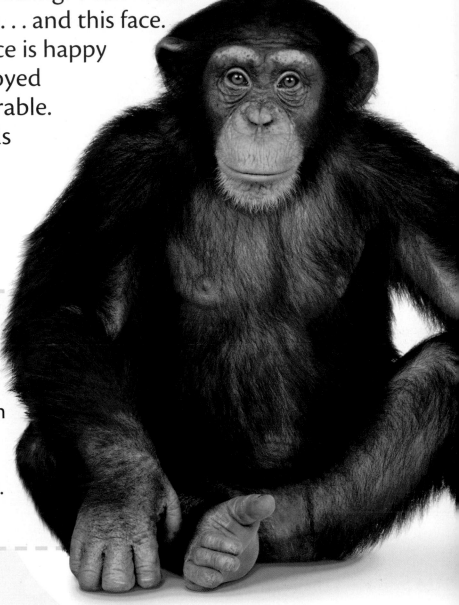

## Synonyms

Synonyms are words that all mean the same thing. When writing, choose the right synonym to tell someone exactly what things are like.

## How it works:

happy → glad, ecstatic, overjoyed

## Examples:

sad → glum, miserable, heartbroken

ask → request, demand, interrogate

## Antonyms

Antonyms are words that mean the opposite. These words help to show someone how things are compared.

## How it works:

speedy / plodding

## Examples:

gigantic / microscopic

scorching / freezing

said

told

asked

shouted

yelled

screamed

cried

whispered

muttered

responded

answered

uttered

argued

chattered

stammered

stuttered

babbled

jabbered

# Size matters

How "big" is this big whale? How "small" is this small clownfish? Create a list of words that mean big and another list for words that mean small.

| Words that mean small | Words that mean big |
|---|---|
| ................................ | ................................ |
| ................................ | ................................ |
| ................................ | ................................ |
| ................................ | ................................ |

**Circle the word that best describes the whale and the clownfish.**

# Showing off!

Suggest five words that mean the same as "beautiful" to describe this peacock.

................................................

................................................

................................................

................................................

................................................

# Best word

Here is a list of synonyms for "red." Which word do you think best describes these "red" animals? You can use a word more than once.

| ruby | scarlet | russet | flushed |
|------|---------|--------|---------|
| flaming | crimson | rosy | |

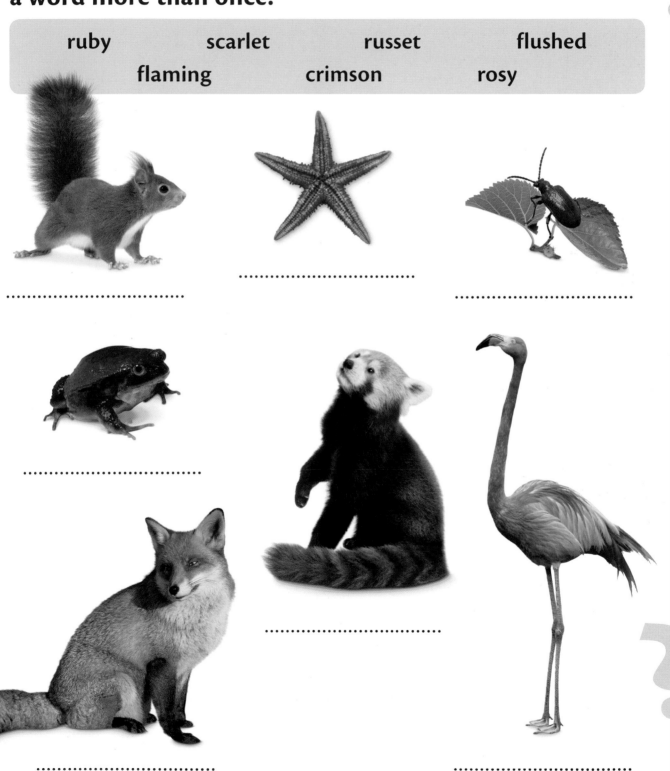

....................................

....................................

....................................

....................................

....................................

....................................

....................................

# In the beginning...

I might be an extinct dinosaur, but I can tell you a thing or two about root words. The word dinosaur literally means "fearfully great lizard" and many dinosaurs like me have the Greek root word "saur" in their names. I'm stegosaurus, which means "roof or covered lizard." Talking about roots is making me feel hungry. I'll get back to munching some plant roots.

## Root words

A root word is the main part of the word to which other parts have been added. Families of words can all be made with the same root word.

## How it works:

camara + **saurus** =
chambered + lizard

## Examples:

ankylo**saurus** = stiff lizard

tyranno**saurus** = tyrant lizard

baro**saurus** = heavy lizard

## Spelling and meaning

If you know how to spell the root word, then this will help with the spelling and the meaning of the words with that root.

## How it works:

**sign** → **sign**ature, **sign**age, **sign**ify
**live** → a**live**, surv**ive**, **live**lihood, re**live**

## Examples:

**phone** = sound

→ tele**phone** = sound that travels far

→ **phone**me = smallest unit of sound

→ head**phone**s, ear**phone**s, homo**phone**, micro**phone**

### Words to learn

sign

signature

live

lively

change

changeable

answer

answerable

early

earliest

extreme

extremely

heart

heartily

popular

popularity

remember

remembrance

# Do- you-think-he-saurus?

Make a collection of dinosaurs with the root word "saurus" and find out their meanings.

| Dinosaur name | Meaning |
| --- | --- |
| ............................................. | ............................................. |
| ............................................. | ............................................. |
| ............................................. | ............................................. |
| ............................................. | ............................................. |
| ............................................. | ............................................. |
| ............................................. | ............................................. |

# Word bank

What other words with these root words can you think of?

| "graph" (Greek = writing) | "hood" (Old English = person, condition, or quality) | "trans" (Latin = across) |
| --- | --- | --- |
| tele**graph** | child**hood** | **trans**late |
| ......................... | ......................... | ......................... |
| ......................... | ......................... | ......................... |
| ......................... | ......................... | ......................... |
| ......................... | ......................... | ......................... |
| ......................... | ......................... | ......................... |

# Root challenge

**Work out the meaning of the original root word (shown in *italic*) in these words. Then add two examples of words with each of these "roots."**

*uni* as in universe ........................................................................

................................................ ................................................

*bi* as in bicycle ........................................................................

................................................ ................................................

*tri* as in triceratops ........................................................................

................................................ ................................................

*quad* as in quadrilateral ........................................................................

................................................ ................................................

*octo* as in octopus ........................................................................

................................................ ................................................

*cent* as in century ........................................................................

................................................ ................................................

*mille* as in millipede ........................................................................

................................................ ................................................

# Glossary

## Adjective
a word that describes a noun; e.g., an *enormous* lion

## Adverb
a word that describes a verb, adjective, or adverb, which tells when, where, or how something happened, often ending **ly**; e.g., John *happily* walked along the road

## Antonym
a word that has an opposite meaning to another; e.g., *big* and *small*

## Compound word
a word formed when two words are joined together; e.g., *football*

## Consonant
the letters of the alphabet that are not vowels

## Contraction
shortened form of words, with an apostrophe denoting the missing letter or letters; e.g., should not becomes *shouldn't*

## Digraph
two letters that combine to make one sound; e.g., *ph, ey*

## Homograph
a word that is spelled the same as another word, but has a different meaning and often sounds different; e.g., *park, bow*

## Homophone
a word that sounds the same as another word, but is spelled differently and has a different meaning; e.g., *dear* and *deer*

## Letter string
a spelling pattern with more than one letter; e.g., *ough, igh*

## Noun
a word that is either an object, a person, or an idea; e.g., *chair, cat,* and *grace* are all nouns

**Phoneme**
the smallest unit of sound a letter or letters make; e.g., *c-a-t* are the phonemes in cat

**Plural**
when there is more than one noun; e.g., three *horses*

**Prefix**
a letter or group of letters that when added to the beginning of another word, changes the meaning; e.g., **mis** makes spell *misspell*

**Root word**
the main part of a word to which other parts are added; e.g., *tricycle*, *triceps*

**Singular**
when there is one of something; e.g., a *cat* or a *mouse*

**Suffix**
a letter or group of letters that when added at the end of another word, changes the meaning and sometimes the spelling of the original word; e.g., happy becomes *happier*

**Synonym**
a word that has a very similar meaning to another word; e.g., *big, large*

**Verb**
a word that describes an action; e.g., *run, jump, think, try*

**Verb tense**
the verb changes according to when it has happened, e.g. in the present—he *is shouting*; in the past—he *shouted*; and in the future—he *will shout*

**Vowel**
the five letters of the alphabet *a, e, i, o, u*

# Answers

**8–9**

### Fill in fun
teams, toys, kisses, girls, weeds, patches, benches, nights, wishes

### The big finish!
witches, wands, cats, spells, wizards

### Super silly sentences
branches, foxes, potions, matches, spells, wands

### Double up
The witches added eyes of frogs, feathers of birds, tails of horses, and scales of fishes.

---

**14–15**

### Two's company
dogs, ducks, bees, foxes

### Word swap
The **wolves** in the dark **woods**
The **babies** in the **cribs**
The **ladies** with **loaves** of bread
The **horseshoes** on the **hooves**

### Odd one out
calf, bear, porcupine

**20–21**

### Sort it out

| Just add "s" | Add "es" | Change to "ies" | Irregular |
|---|---|---|---|
| snakes<br>monkeys<br>armadillos<br>eagles<br>penguins | foxes<br>fishes | butterflies<br>wallabies<br>ponies | mice<br>moose |

---

**30–31**

### Right or wrong?
danceing, growlling, fixxed, joging, explord

### Double or not

| Double the consonant for past tense | Do not double the consonant for past tense |
|---|---|
| hopped, stopped, slipped, planned | noticed, groaned, used, liked, shared, enjoyed, asked |

### Odd one out
hug, bake, count, run

---

**36–37**

### You choose!
The hippo is **larger** than the zebra.
The little monkey can climb into the **highest** branches of the trees.
The antelope can run **faster** than the bison.
The water buffalo is the **muddiest** of all the animals at the waterhole.
The tiger is the **fiercest** of all the big cats.

### Compare challenge
lion cub – youngest
giraffe – tallest
hippo – heaviest
rabbit – smallest

### Fill in fun
loud, louder, loudest
quiet, quieter, quietest
scary, scarier, scariest
large, larger, largest
noisy, noisier, noisiest

### 40–41

**Choose a suffix**
restful, beautiful, enjoyment, colourless or colourful, naughtiness

**Find the meaning**
harmless, kindness, cheerful, movement

**Missing word**
kindness, harmless, cheerful, movement, careless

---

### 44–45

**Whose home?**
the chickens' coop, the horses' stable, the bees' hive, the fishes' aquarium, the beaver's lodge, the badgers' burrow, the doves' dovecot, the cow's barn

**Right the wrong**
The girl got the **horse's** saddle from the rack.
The **mice's** nest was snug and dry.
The **pig's** supper was some acorns, which it ate very quickly.
It is **Ibrahim's** birthday today.
I went to the **children's** playground with my friends.
The **leopard's** fur is covered with a spotted pattern.

**Time challenge**
the ladies' cats
the pig's sty
the bear's fur
the buffaloes' hooves
the wolf's lair

---

### 48–49

**Fill in fun**
fly, magnify, comply, deny; lion

**You choose!**
The tiger cubs **rely** on their mother.
The students **apply** for the job.
The witnesses **identify** the thief.
The desert was **dry**.

**Word sort**

| /igh/ sound: | /ee/ sound: |
|---|---|
| fry | happy |
| apply | ordinary |
| supply | century |
| why | probably |
| imply | lazy |
| July | actually |
| rely | |

---

### 52–53

**Clue 1**

| soft "g" | hard "g" |
|---|---|
| giant, giraffe, general, gem, germ, ginger | goat, get, gum, game, glad, gear, good, grape |

**Conclusion**
When I went to the zoo, I saw a <u>huge range</u> of animals. There were <u>large giraffes</u> and a (great gecko). The (goats) tried to (get) my (gloves)! Looking suspicious was the <u>giant</u> panda but I also suspected the (grizzly) bear, which (greeted) me with a sort of smile as I (gazed) through the (glass).

---

### 56–57

**Fill in fun**
disappearing, unhappy, discovered, uncertain, mistake

**What's the opposite?**
undress, discomfort misbehave, misunderstand, disconnect

**All change!**
My brother disagreed with me.
The rider dismounted the horse.

### 62–63

**Missing word**
quietly, lightly, accidentally, bravely, possibly

**All change!**
naughtily, specially, strangely, surprisingly, peculiarly, regularly, carefully, easily, suddenly

**Answers** 125

### 66–67

**Fiction quiz**
Goldilocks
Alice
Goats
Chicken Little
Eat the pigs

**Happy endings**
discussion, imagination,
authorization, creation,
description, expression, revision

---

### 70–71

**Missing words**
These are fine **grey** coloured horses, each with long **reins** for the riders to hold. In winter, when it is snowy, they sometimes pull a **sleigh**. They make a loud noise called **neighing**. **They** stay in a **stable** at night and there are **eight** stalls altogether. Each one has a beautifully cared for **mane**.

**Add the labels**
crayons, tray, weigh, reindeer, plane, acorn, train

---

### 74–75

**Dear deer**
How are you? I have been meaning **to** write **to** you for **two** weeks now, but I have been **too** busy at school. We have been learning all about homophones. How are things in the forest? If you'd like **to** catch up, meet me at **two** o'clock. Bring your friends the squirrels, **too**.
From me!

**Silly sentences**
I couldn't wait to **meet** my friends.
Because I overslept, I **missed** the bus.
I had a long **wait** for the next bus.
The mouse got his **tail** caught.

**You choose!**
The boat sailed in **fair** weather.
Dad **missed** the train to work.
The boy ties a **knot** with his shoelaces.
The tired storekeeper took a **break**.
The lion had a majestic **mane**.

---

### 78–79

**Match up!**
interrupt, submerge, antibiotic, return, automatic

**Which one?**
intercepted, interact, interlock
subtract, submarine, subject
autocracy, autopilot, automobile
reaffirm, record, reheat
antisocial, anticlimax, antidote

**You choose!**
I am going to **recycle** these bottles.
When Suzy kept talking, the teacher asked her to please not **interrupt** in the middle of the lesson.
In the intermission of a show, you can buy **refreshments**.
The famous film star was asked for his **autograph**.
The crocodile was completely **submerged** under the water.

### Cat rescue
we had, should not, did not, must not, will not, she is, she would, she is, it had, was not, she had

### One-minute challenge
he's, don't, that'll, couldn't

### You choose!
I've got **your** book by mistake.
**They're** going to the farm by bus.
**Whose** coat is that?
**It's** a really sunny day today.

---

### Word sort

| c = /k/ | c = /s/ | c = /sh/ | c = /q/ | c = /x/ |
|---------|---------|----------|---------|---------|
| carrot | cylinder | magician | cue | access |
| cardigan | celebrity | ocean | | accident |
| column | mercy | | | except |
| disco | cereal | | | |
| Canada | celery | | | |
| octopus | December | | | |

---

### Quiz master
calf, February, Science, vegetable, knife and scissors, island, chocolate

### Letter hunt
**w**rinkle, san**d**wich, int**e**rest, clim**b**, listen, g**u**ide, **w**rapping, **k**neel, s**c**ience, bis**c**uit, **g**nash, dis**g**uise, fore**i**gn, cas**t**le

---

### Word sort

| /off/ | /uff/ | /o/ | /aw/ | /oo/ |
|-------|-------|-----|------|------|
| cough | rough | borough | ought | through |
| trough | enough | thorough | bought | slough |
| | tough | dough | thought | |
| | | although | | |

---

### Match the meaning
fine – A charge made for overdue items or illegally parked cars
duck – A verb meaning to move your head down quickly
wind – A strong gust of air
saw – A sharp, serrated edged cutting tool
watch – A verb meaning to look at

---

### Match up!
goalkeeper, sunshine, bluebell, birthday, everybody or everyone, paintbrush, breakfast, anybody or anyone, backbone, fairground, halftime, upstairs

### Double or not
tentacles
beetle
prickles
turtle
waddles

**Senior Editor** Deborah Lock
**Editor** Arpita Nath
**Asst. Editor** Kritika Gupta
**Canadian Editor** Barbara Campbell
**Canadian Consultant** Marilyn Wilson
**Senior Art Editor** Ann Cannings
**Project Art Editor** Tanvi Nathyal
**Art Editors** Ian Midson, Roohi Rais
**Picture Researcher** Sakshi Saluja
**Jacket Designer** Dheeraj Arora
**Managing Editor** Soma B. Chowdhury
**Art Director** Martin Wilson
**DTP Designers** Nand Kishor Acharya,
Ashok Kumar, Mohd. Rizwan, Dheeraj Singh
**Producer, Pre-Production** Dragana Puvacic
**Producer** Priscilla Reby

First Canadian Edition, 2016

DK Canada
320 Front Street West, Suite 1400
Toronto, Ontario M5V 3B6
First published in Great Britain in 2016 by
Dorling Kindersley Limited

ISBN 978-1-55363-275-7

DK books are available at special discounts when purchased
in bulk for corporate sales, sales promotions, premiums, fund-raising, or
educational use. For details, please contact specialmarkets@dk.com.

Printed and bound in China.

The publisher would like to thank the following for
their kind permission to reproduce their photographs:
(Key: a-above; b-below/bottom; c-centre; f-far; l-left; r-right; t-top)
1 **Dreamstime.com:** Mythja (tl). 7 **Dorling Kindersley:** Neil
Fletcher (bl, bc). 9 **Dorling Kindersley:** Cecil Williamson Collection (crb). 10
**Dreamstime.com:** Happyshoot (c). 12-13 **Fotolia:** Eric Isselee (t). 12 **Fotolia:**
Eric Isselee (bl, bc). 19 **Fotolia:** Eric Isselee (bl, bc). 20 **iStockphoto.com:**
thawats (cla). 24 **Dreamstime.com:** Uros Petrovic (tl). 25 **Dreamstime.com:**
Uros Petrovic (tr, clb). 29 **Getty Images:** Jason Edwards (cb). 32 **Getty Images:**
Nicole Duplaix (tl). 32-33 **Corbis:** David Watts / Visuals Unlimited. 36
**Dreamstime.com:** Johannes Gerhardus Swanepoel (cr). **Fotolia:** Eric Isselee (cl).
37 **Dreamstime.com:** Eric Isselee (ca). **Fotolia:** Eric Isselee (cl). 40 **Fotolia:** Eric
Isselee (cra). 42-43 **Corbis:** Klaus Mehret / BIA / Minden Pictures (t). 44
**Dreamstime.com:** Theo Malings (ca, br); Vchphoto (cla). 45 **Dorling
Kindersley:** Jerry Young (cr). 49 **Fotolia:** Eric Isselee (cra). 51 **Dreamstime.com:**
Mythja (b). 54-55 **Dreamstime.com:** Samfoto (Background). 56 **123RF.com:**
Iakov Filimonov (tr). 59 **Dreamstime.com:** Marusea Turcu (tr). 62 **Dorling
Kindersley:** Natural History Museum, London (br). 68 **Dreamstime.com:**
Stuartbur (bl). 68-69 **Getty Images:** Tim Graham. 71 **Dorling Kindersley:**
The Real Aeroplane Company (c). **Dreamstime.com:** Simone Winkler /
Eyecatchlight (cl). **iStockphoto.com:** Floortje (tc). 72-73 **123RF.com:** Elena
Duvernay. 74 **Dreamstime.com:** Sombra12 (ca). 75 **Dreamstime.com:** Melissa
King (c). 76-77 **Getty Images:** Brian J. Skerry (t). 78 **Dorling Kindersley:** Jerry
Young (br). 80 **Dorling Kindersley:** Jerry Young (tr). **Dreamstime.com:** Eric
Isselee (crb). 84-85 **Corbis:** Viewstock. 85 **Dreamstime.com:** 350jb (ca). 86
**123RF.com:** Iakov Filimonov (tr). 90-91 **naturepl.com:** Jabruson. 102-103
**Dorling Kindersley:** Odds Farm Park, High Wycombe, Bucks. 103 **123RF.com:**
damianpalus (c). 108 **Dreamstime.com:** Tropper2000 (cra). 110 **Dorling
Kindersley:** Liberty's Owl, Raptor and Reptile Centre, Hampshire, UK (bl). 112
**123RF.com:** Isabelle Kõhn (cl); Konstantin Kalishko (cl). **Alamy Images:** Brian
Hagiwara (tr). 114-115 **123RF.com:** Eric Isselee. 114 **123RF.com:** Eric Isselee
(bl). 115 **iStockphoto.com:** GlobalP (bl). 116 **Corbis:** Eric and David Hosking
(br). **Dreamstime.com:** Musat Christian (cr). **Fotolia:** uwimages (cl). 117
**123RF.com:** Eric Isselee (cla, cb); Kati Molin (ca). **Dorling Kindersley:** British
Wildlife Centre, Surrey, UK (bl). **Dreamstime.com:** Sombra12 (br). **iStockphoto.
com:** DreamyHarry (cra). 122 **Dreamstime.com:** Isselee (tl). 123 **123RF.com:**
Kseniya Abramova (cla). 124 **Fotolia:** Eric Isselee (br). 125 **Fotolia:** Eric Isselee
(tr, cl). 126 **Dorling Kindersley:** Jerry Young (br). **Dreamstime.com:** Sombra12
(cr). 127 **123RF.com:** Konstantin Kalishko (br)
**Jacket images: Front:** Dreamstime.com: Milos Tasic (tl)

All other images © Dorling Kindersley
For further information see: www.dkimages.com

A WORLD OF IDEAS:
SEE ALL THERE IS TO KNOW
www.dk.com

# Notes for parents

Spelling in English is not that easy. There are many rules and many exceptions to the rules and also some words that follow no rule at all! Children need to be encouraged to try out spelling and gain confidence to spell independently. They need to build up skills so that they are not reliant on adults or dictionaries to make a good attempt at spelling an unfamiliar word.

Reading is a great help with spelling, and it actually does not matter what they are reading. Your child could love comics, or hockey magazines, fiction or non-fiction; it is the quantity and reading for pleasure that makes the difference. Reading a lot exposes children to the spellings, so they start to recognize when they have spelled something wrong because it does not look right on the page.

Children should also start by using phonics and what they know about spelling for their first attempt. If a very young child uses what they know about phonics to spell a word, they are starting well and using the correct skills. Older children start to recognize some of the other spelling conventions as well.

This book teaches the spelling rules, where they exist, but also looks at how children learn spellings, encouraging them to find the ways that suit them best. Trying out spelling is a good way of seeing if it looks right and should be encouraged as an important part of the learning process.

It is also important to consider spelling as a tool, not an end goal. It is useful because it enables us to become better writers. If we learn how to spell a great word and use it in writing, this is more important than being able to spell a great many words but not use the words when we write. If you see spelling as part of the writing process, you will be helping your child to become a better writer, not just a better speller.